How to

Use paper and card

Gerry Downes
photographs by Graham Murrell

Studio Vista

Acknowledgments

The author is indebted to Martin Gardner's excellent 'Mathematical puzzles and diversions' and 'More mathematical puzzles and diversions', and to H. M. Cundy and A. P. Rollett's 'Mathematical models' (second edition)

Studio Vista a division of
Cassell & Collier Macmillan Publishers Limited
35 Red Lion Square, London WCIR 4SG
Sydney, Auckland, Toronto, Johannesburg

An affiliate of the Macmillan Publishing Co. Inc.
New York

Filmset and printed by BAS Printers Limited, Wallop, Hampshire

ISBN 0 289 70552 5

Contents

Introduction   7
Materials and tools   8
Origami   9
Simple paper folding   11
Tricks and games   17
Mathematical solids   19
Mathematical games and puzzles   36
Colour collages   50
Paper sculpture   53
Sound effects   65
Suppliers   67
Index   68

Introduction

Paper can be folded, creased, cut and moulded into startlingly beautiful forms. It can show in a practical way the answer to complicated mathematical puzzles, ranging from pure polyhedra to weird flexible hexagons and strips with only one side and one edge. In addition, paper can be used to make incredible sound effects, from gunfire to music.

Where nets (this is a mathematical term meaning a pattern) are given in this book, you can either fold them and tape the edges across with Sellotape, or you can add glue flaps. Flaps are only indicated where they are strictly necessary. If you want to add flaps anywhere, they should be drawn on *alternate* edges.

There are few rules to follow except the golden one; the sculptures should be fun to make, even if they are sometimes difficult, and the end results should be beautiful to look at.

Materials and tools

Naturally the main material is paper and the stiffer it is the easier the models will be to make. Thin card and patterned paper are useful as well. You won't need to buy a lot of special papers. Experiment with whatever is easily available first, and buy only if you need to.

Start a collection of things such as:
paper bags
newspapers
magazines
cereal boxes
wrapping paper
greaseproof paper etc.

Tools
You need:
scissors
craft knives
ruler
set square
protractor
compasses
metal straight edge
hard pencils
paste and glue

For some things you may find it useful to have:
punch
staple gun
paper clips and fasteners
Sellotape
double stick tape

Origami

One of the most famous, and, possibly the oldest of the origami folded animals is this bird.

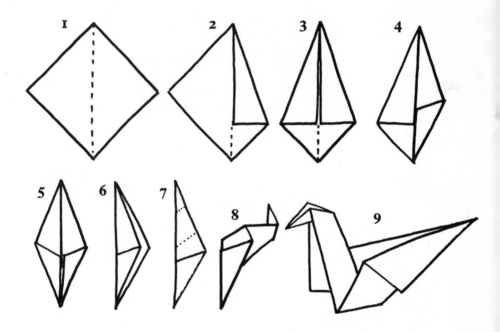

This is a more complex one, the wing-flapping swan.

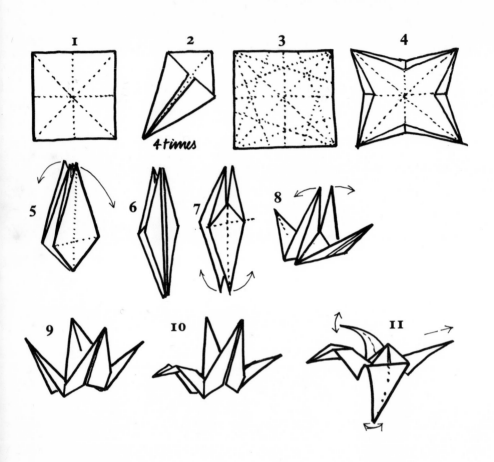

Once you have made these two birds, you have handled most of the basic origami folds. Try experimenting with these folds to make other paper models. Here are some suggestions.

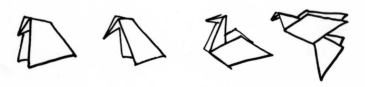

Simple paper folding

Many of these will be familiar to you already but some will be new and some will be surprise variations.

Paper boats

This is the classic way to fold a paper boat. Newspaper is the best paper to use for boats.

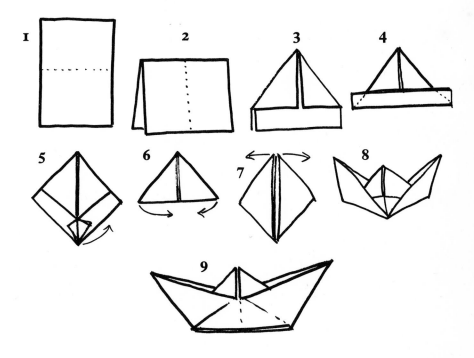

If you start with a large sheet of paper, stage seven does nicely as a hat. In fact the boat itself makes a nice hat – wear it sideways like Napoleon.

Here are a couple of variations. The final step in each of these is to turn the whole thing inside out.

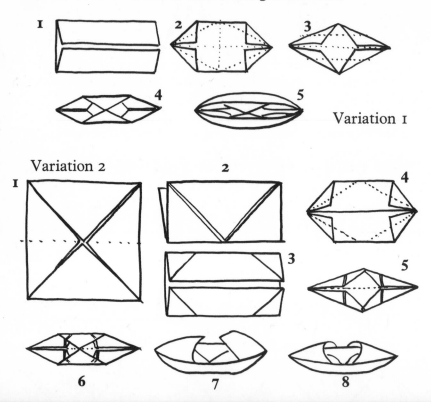

Variation 1

Variation 2

Paper aeroplanes

This is the classic way of folding a paper aeroplane. Experiment with the length of the tail and the degree of fold of the wings, or add paper clips to the nose, until you get a good level flight.

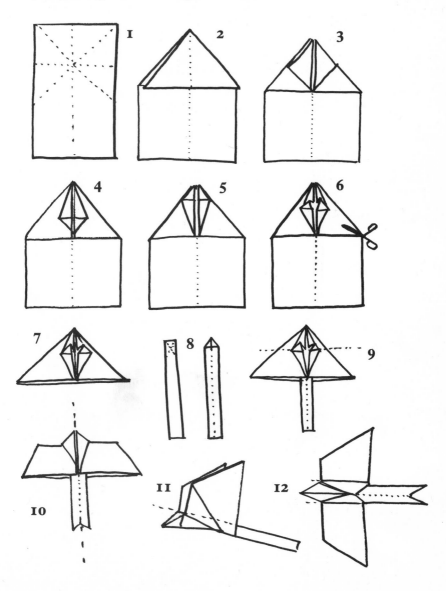

This is the classic fold for a paper dart. A paper clip on the nose will improve the performance.

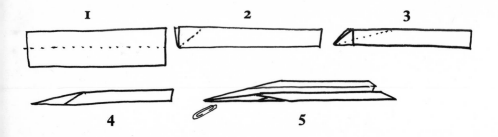

Helicopters

These helicopters can be made from any scraps of paper you can find. You will be surprised at just how many shapes can perform perfectly, so long as the lower half is heavy enough.

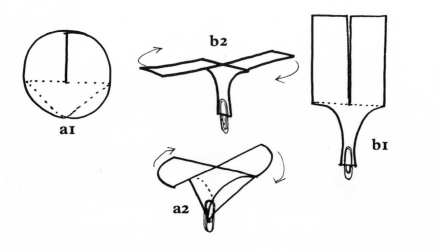

Paper hats

One of the simplest ways of making a paper hat is to use a large brown paper bag, a shopping bag, or even an abandoned record sleeve. This gives you a firm shape that only needs decorating. Another excellent hat is a large manilla envelope. The flap makes a marvellous soldier-like peak. On a used envelope you will have to steam open the flap. Here are some ideas for transforming such paper bags.

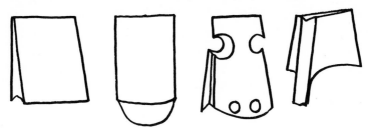

Some effective hats can be folded from sheets of newspaper. Here is the most well-known one.

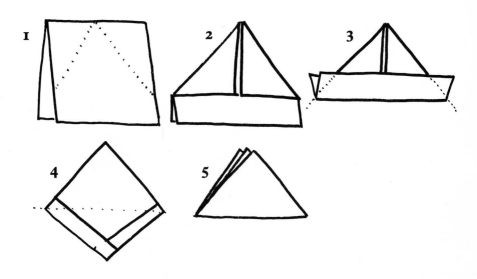

And this is a variation on that basic theme.

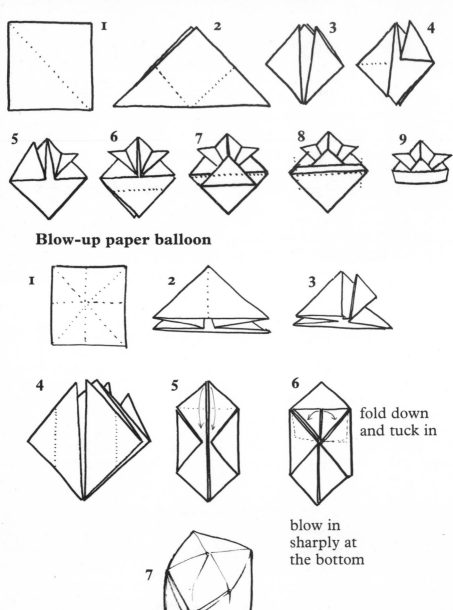

Blow-up paper balloon

fold down
and tuck in

blow in
sharply at
the bottom

Tricks and games

Waterlily napkins

Paper napkins can be made into flowers for elegant table decorations for parties.

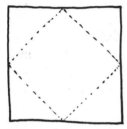 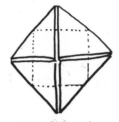

1 start with a square napkin

2 fold the points to the centre

3 fold the points to the centre again; turn it over

4 fold the points to the centre

5 pull the points from the back round and up but don't pull them completely out

The fastest scrunch in the West

Two players face each other. Each one holding a large sheet of newspaper by one corner. At the word 'Go' each player scrunches the sheet up into a ball. He may use only one hand, with no help from the other hand, and no touching of the body. The first player to complete the scrunch and throw the ball of paper at his opponent wins.

Tricks

How to float a needle on a glass of water
First, drop a piece of tissue paper on the surface of the
water. Then carefully drop the needle on the paper.
Once the paper is saturated it will sink to the bottom
leaving the needle floating on the top. If you magnetize
the needle, by stroking it with a magnet, it will behave
like a compass needle.

How to hold a glass of water upside down
Fill the glass to the brim with water. Take a thin sheet
of card and lay it on the top. Holding the card in place
turn the glass upside down. Now take your hand away
and the card will stay in place and keep the water in the
glass.

How to link two paper clips by magic

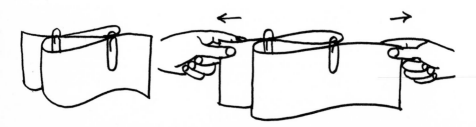

Take a strip of fairly stiff paper, bend it into a serpentine
(S bend) loop and place the two paper clips as shown.
Pull sharply on the two ends and the clips will fly off
linked together.

Mathematical solids

There are five Platonic solids and one of them is very familiar, the cube.

The five solids are:
1 The tetrahedron with 4 sides (all triangles)
2 The cube with six sides (all square)
3 The octahedron with 8 sides (all triangles)
4 The dodecahedron with 12 sides (all pentagons)
5 The icosahedron with 20 sides (all triangles)

The solids are easy to construct and make into gifts or decorations. Filled with sand or weighted in some way they make marvellous paperweights.

Tetrahedron

A very simple way to make a tetrahedron is to take an envelope and seal it. Draw an equalilateral triangle, with all three sides the same length, on one end. Cut along the dotted line from **a** to **b**.

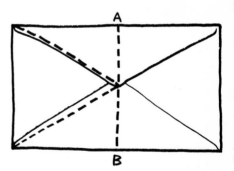

Hold point **a** with one hand and point **b** with the other hand. Push **a** and **b** towards each other until they meet.

Tape up the open end.

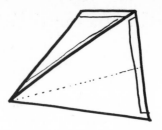

Make eight of these and tape or glue them together edge to edge.

How to make a puzzle tetrahedron
Cut out two nets, **a**.

Fold the nets and tape or glue the openings to make two identical shapes, **b**.

These two shapes can be stood together in a special way, to form a tetrahedron. In case you can't work out how to do it, the solution is on page 24.

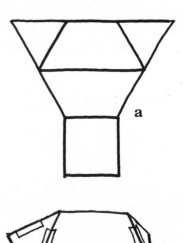

a

b

Cuboctahedron

This can be made from the net on page 22. Tape the edges together. Use narrow coloured, rather than clear, Sellotape. Or, add glue flaps (the dotted lines) to alternate edges and paste or glue them together. This will make it look neater.

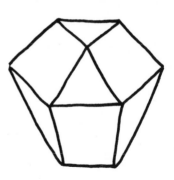

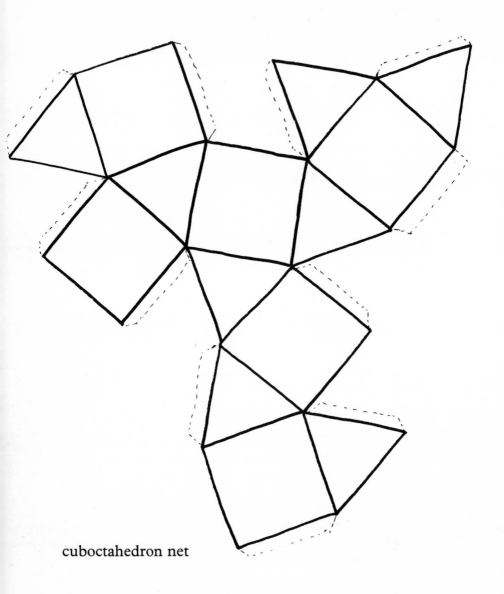

cuboctahedron net

Octahedron

To make an eight-sided die, draw and cut out the octahedral net and number the sides.

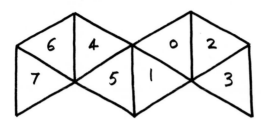

The die will not roll very well, so it is best to flip it in the air.

Mind reading trick

With this die you can work a mind reading trick. Ask a friend to choose a number between 0 and 7 inclusive. Hold up the die so that the numbers 1 3 5 7 are towards him and ask him if he can see his number. If he answers 'yes' count 1, if he answers 'no' count 0.

Then turn the die so that he sees numbers 2 3 6 7 and ask again if he sees his number. A 'yes' for these numbers counts 2, and a 'no' counts as 0.

Finally turn the die so that he sees 4 5 6 7 and ask once more if he sees his number. This time count 4 for a 'yes' and again 'no' counts 0. Total the score for the 'yeses' and you will have the number he chose.

Number the corners that will face *you*, 1, 2, 3, so that you know which side is facing your friend, and which side comes first, second and third. Rehearse a bit before you try it on anyone.

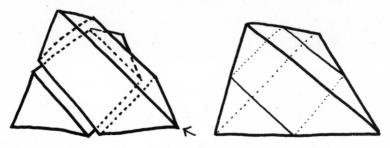

Opposite
The large figure at the top is a tetrahedron, with four
triangular sides (see page 19).
From left to right are:
a dodecahedron with twelve sides (see page 26)
a square-based pyramid spike (see page 30)
an octahedron, or eight-sided die (see page 23)
an icosahedron with twenty triangular sides (see page
  29)

Dodecahedron

One of the most attractive of the five Platonic solids, the dodecahedron, is made up of twelve pentagons.

To draw a pentagon, first draw a circle. Then use a protractor to mark off five lines at angles of 72 degrees each, from the centre of the circle. Join the points where the lines touch the edge of the circle and you have a pentagon.

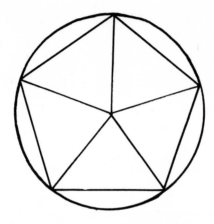

Make a card template of a pentagon and draw round it to make the net on page 27. Cut the whole thing out as one piece. Score the dotted lines, so that the dodecahedron is easier to fold. Tape or glue the edges together.

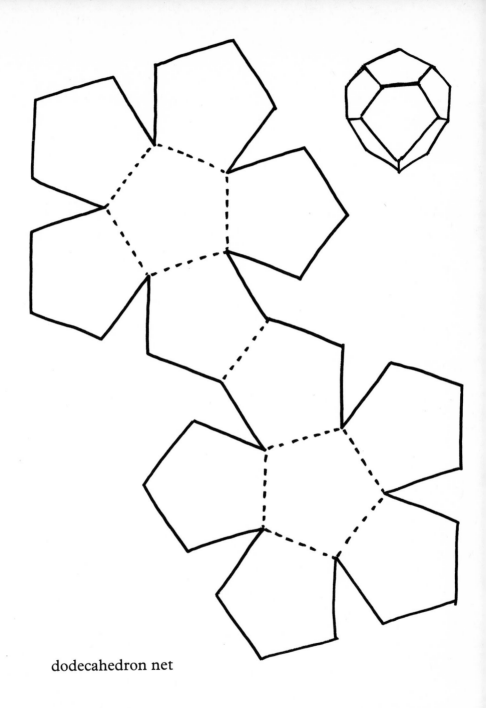

dodecahedron net

A pop-up dodecahedron

Draw and cut out the two nets. Score and fold inwards along the edges of the inner pentagons. Place the two face to face so that the bends face inwards and the points overlap. Now weave an elastic band around the points, passing over and under. When you release it the dodecahedron will spring into shape. For this figure, the stiffer the card the better. Since it has twelve sides it makes a good desk calendar.

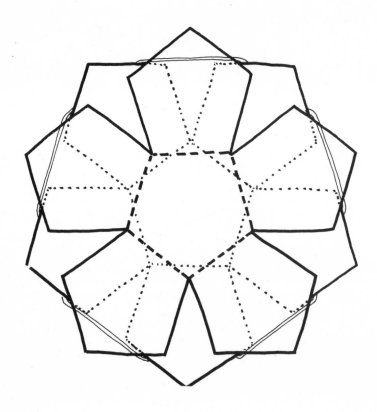

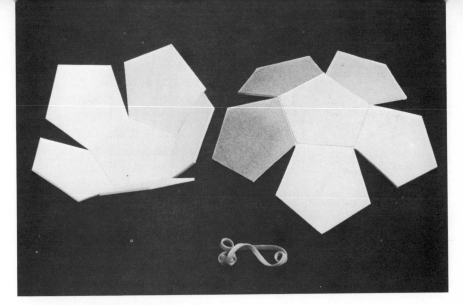

The icosahedron

This is an elegant solid with twenty triangular sides. Draw and cut out the net. The triangles should each have three 60 degree angles. Make a fold along all the dotted lines. Join **a** to **a** and **b** to **b** and then join the top and bottom triangles. Use coloured tape or add glue flaps.

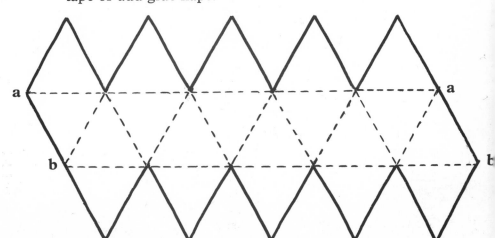

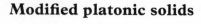

Modified platonic solids

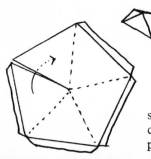

triangular base pyramid spike
for cuboctahedron from
a square

The cactus-like
icosahedron was made by
stapling together triangular
pieces with a triangle
folded in each one
(see diagram page 32).
Alongside the cactus is a
cuboctahedron with
pyramid spikes stuck
on its triangular facets.
You could make a cubocta-
hedron with pyramid
spikes that have a square
base to fit onto square
facets.

square base pyramid for
cuboctahedron from a
pentagon

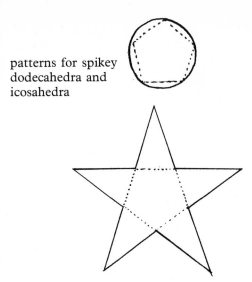

patterns for spikey
dodecahedra and
icosahedra

The rounded dodecahedron
(on the left in the photograph)
is constructed from 12
circles with a pentagon
folded in them. The spikey
one is made with 12 five
pointed stars. The
circular dodecahedron has
been stuck with glue.

The icosahedron with curved ridges (bottom left) is composed of circles with a triangle folded in each one, **a**. The spikey one was made from 20 triangular pieces with a triangle folded in each, **b**. The open icosahedron (bottom right) is made from open triangles stapled together.

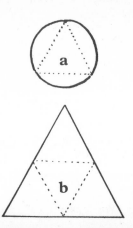

Opposite
The top picture shows a spikey blue/green icosahedron and a rounded black/olive icosahedron (see page 29). The bottom one shows a yellow/white/mauve dodecahedron and a gold spikey dodecahedron (see page 26) These can be hung as decorations, or filled with sand to make paperweights

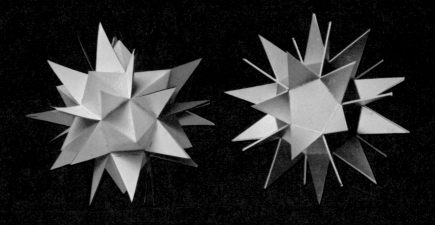

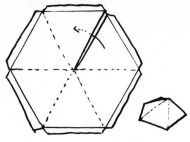

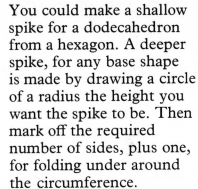

You could make a shallow spike for a dodecahedron from a hexagon. A deeper spike, for any base shape is made by drawing a circle of a radius the height you want the spike to be. Then mark off the required number of sides, plus one, for folding under around the circumference.

shallow spike for dodecahedron folded from a hexagon. Add glue flaps

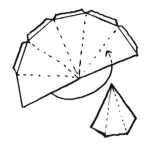

deeper spike

Opposite
Scarlet/magenta cuboctahedron (see page 22) yellow/ green and red/green dodecahedra (see page 26). These beautiful shapes are not too difficult to make, and make lovely, unusual presents

Mathematical games and puzzles

Mobius strip

This is a piece of paper with only one side.

Take a long strip of paper and make it into a loop, but give it a single twist before you join the ends. It now has only one side and only one edge.

Prove this by drawing a pencil line continuously down the centre, without lifting the pencil, until you get back to your starting point. You will have drawn a line along the centre of both 'sides' of the strip. It is called a Mobius strip after the man who invented it.

Imagine a giant strip of metal in this form orbiting in space. If two spacemen wearing magnetic boots were to start in the position shown below and walk off in opposite directions, they would meet face to face half way round, though neither would have crossed from his 'side' to the other's.

Cutting up Mobius strips

There are other strange properties of Mobius strips. Try the following experiments:

1 Cut along the centre line of a Mobius strip until you return to your starting point. Pause before you cut the last bit and try to guess what will happen. Do the pencil test on the resulting strip.

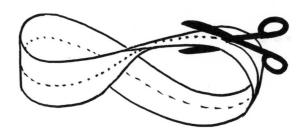

2 Make a similar cut all round another Mobius strip but start one third of the way in from one edge. It will take longer than the first cut and don't be put off by seeing your starting point pass by half way round; keep on cutting one third from the edge.

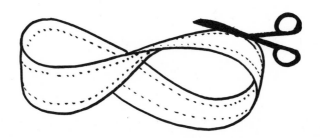

3 Take two strips of paper, lay them on top of each other and twist and hold the ends together. Slip two of the ends in between the opposite two ends. Glue the top two together and the bottom two together to make a double Mobius strip. Slide a short length of card between the two strips and you will be able to run it all round the continuous gap. Now pull the 'two' apart. Do the pencil test.

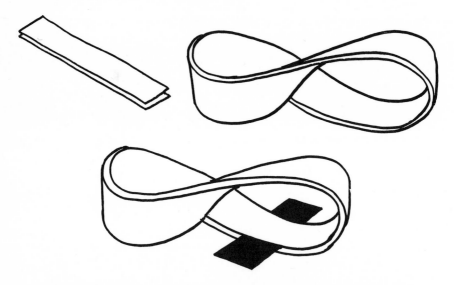

4 Put the strip back as it was, or if this is too difficult, make a new double Mobius strip. Slip a fairly long strip of paper all round in between the other two strips, and join its ends.
Now pull the double Mobius apart again.

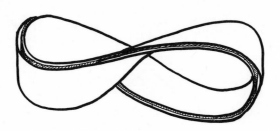

Flexagons (Flexible hexagons)

These fascinating objects were invented in 1939 by Arthur Stone, an English mathematician, then working in America.

You need a strip of paper about 2·5 cm (or 1 in) wide marked off in 10 equilateral triangles, **a**. The triangles must have 60 degree angles.

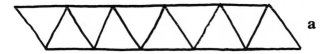

Fold the strip under along the side of the third triangle, **b**.

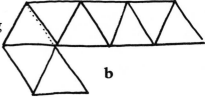

Fold it over along the side of the sixth triangle, **c**. Tuck triangle **d** under the triangle it is lying over.

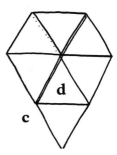

Turn the flexagon over and glue down the last triangle, **e**.

Flexing a flexagon

Fold the flexagon in half, away from you.

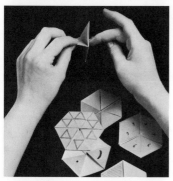

Pinch together two triangles, next to each other, on one side. Push downwards the side you are not holding and flatten it up against the triangles you are holding, at right angles to them.

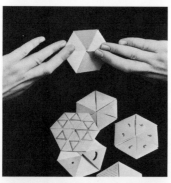

Gently try to peel the flat side away from the point at the top. If you find it will not peel away easily, turn the flexagon and fold it in half again so that you are pinching two different adjacent triangles. It works with only some of them.

As it peels away, release the pinched triangles and the flexagon will turn inside out.

How many faces does the flexagon have?
Make a flexagon from a sheet of two-coloured paper.
Colour in one of the triangular segments in a different
colour and start to flex.
You will find you can turn up three different faces.

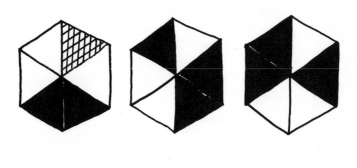

Try decorating one of the
faces with a few dots.

You will seem to have many variations, but really
they are just mirror images of each other.

A more complex flexagon

Mark off a longer strip in 19 equilateral triangles. Number the two sides as in the diagram. Use two-colour paper or hand colour the two sides of the strip differently yourself.

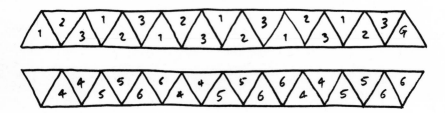

Now fold the strip into a flexagon.

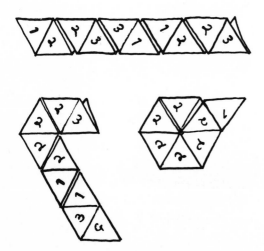

You should have all '1s' on one side and all '2s' on the other. There are six different faces to this flexagon.

Start at one corner and flex there continuously until the flexagon won't open any more, then shift clockwise to the next corner. Always shift in the same direction.

Hints

For making flexagons, particularly the shaped chain type, it is very useful to have some isometric detail paper. This has a blue grid of 60 degree triangles printed all over it, rather as graph paper has squares. You can use this for marking off the chains of triangles as you need them. You will find it useful for some of the Platonic solid nets too.

Flexagons will flex more easily if you fold the strips both ways along the scored lines. The scoring is best done with a hard pencil as you mark out the strips.

For pasting up use Cow Gum or Copydex or Gripfix, which will not make wrinkles in thin paper.

Bambi staplers are useful, though a bit frail. Plier type staplers are excellent but expensive to buy, so see if you can borrow one.

When working with white paper, be scrupulous about washing your hands, or it will end up looking very soiled.

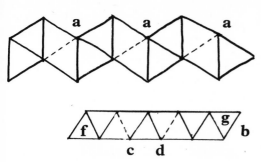

g = glue flaps

Even more complex flexagons

This time, fold a flexagon from a shaped chain of triangles in this 'saw-tooth' pattern. Fold the zig-zag over and over along the three dotted lines, **a**, from left to right, to arrive at a straight strip, **b**.

To make the flexagon, fold line **c** under and line **d** over. Tuck triangle **f** under the triangle it is lying over and glue flap **g** down onto flap **f**.

If you start with two-coloured paper your flexagon should have one face all one colour and the other of alternately coloured triangles.

There are six faces to turn up. They will be difficult to find. Try first to turn up a face of all the second colour.

Draw a face with two eyes and a mouth, on one side. It will turn several times before you get it back in the original form.

45

One last flexagon
Make a zig-zag of triangles.
Fold the zig-zag into a
strip by first folding **a**,
then **b**, over. Then fold **c**
and **d** over, and finally fold
e and **f** under.

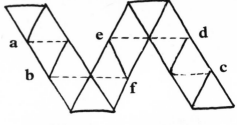

To fold it into a flexagon,
fold four triangles on the
right under and down. And
fold three on the left over
and down. Tuck the last
triangle on the left under.
Turn the flexagon over and
stick the glue flap down.

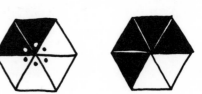

Try drawing six dots on one face close to the centre.
Flex a few times and see for how long you can lose the
dots. Start again with the dots visible. Flex once and
shift to another corner, either way, and flex twice on
the same spot. (If you can't, go back to the start and
shift in the opposite direction.) Thereafter shift
position continually as you flex and the dots will remain
hidden.

46

Decorating flexagons

The interesting thing about these flexagons is that the triangular faces rotate as they are turned inside out. Make decorations of rows of dots, faces or triangles and see what happens when you flex.

sequence **1** **a**   **b**   **c**

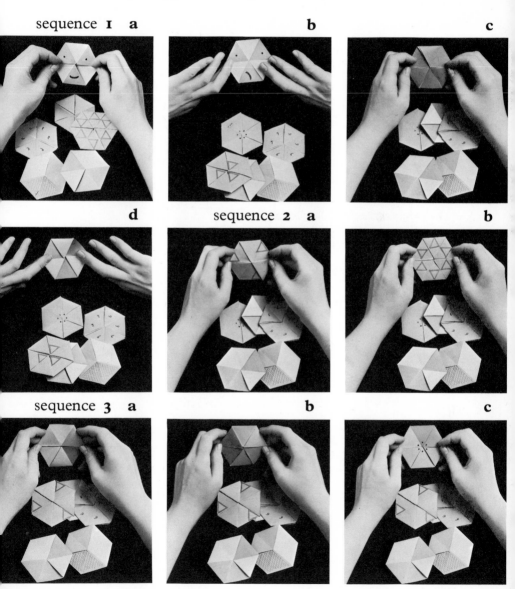

d   sequence **2** **a**   **b**

sequence **3** **a**   **b**   **c**

47

Flexagons based on squares

Flexagons can be based on squares as well as triangles. Cut a chain of six squares and colour it on both sides as shown.

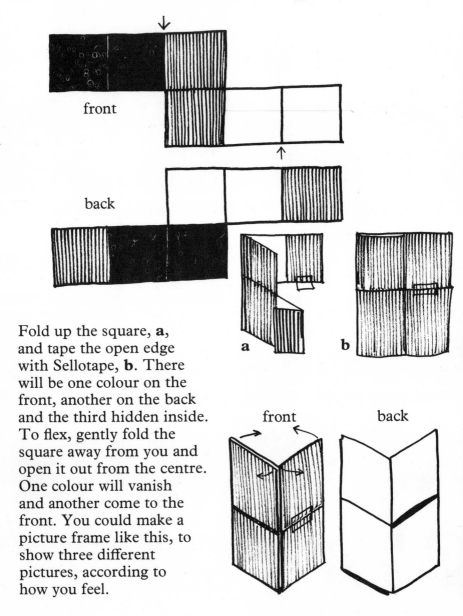

front

back

a

b

Fold up the square, **a**, and tape the open edge with Sellotape, **b**. There will be one colour on the front, another on the back and the third hidden inside. To flex, gently fold the square away from you and open it out from the centre. One colour will vanish and another come to the front. You could make a picture frame like this, to show three different pictures, according to how you feel.

front

back

48

Fiddle cubes

Make this toy by attaching four cubes to a square flexagon. Here is the net for the cubes.

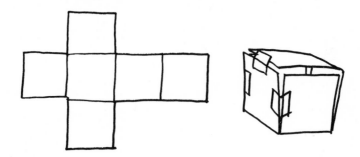

One face of the flexagon never goes inside. Glue the four cubes to that face. You will find that you can flex the cubes just like the strip, but also you can fold them across the normal hinge direction. This is how the movement works. The spots are to show how the cubes are rotating.

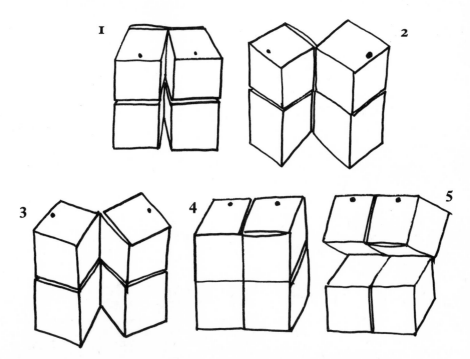

Colour collages

Paper offcuts can be used for composing collage pictures. These are fun to do, and make excellent presents.

Use white card or stiff coloured cartridge for the basic background, and stick the offcuts with Copydex or paste. If you use coloured tissue papers, use Lepage's glue because it enhances the transparency. Make use of texture as well as colour by sticking down all kinds of papers. Sandpaper would make a very good rough surface. Try crumpling it and sticking it down so that the creases show.

The picture opposite, and the one on the cover show two different techniques. The head on the cover is entirely made up of cut-out forms, and the tiger is roughly torn paper to show the shape of the body. Tear some of the strips away from yourself and others towards yourself. This will give you some strips edged with white and some not.

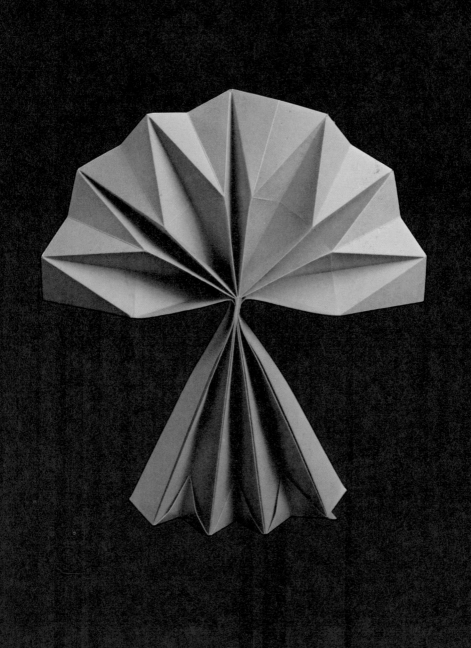

Paper sculpture

Folding

These are the basic folds to enable you to make the architectural forms pictured on page 55. The solid lines in the diagrams mean 'fold this side', the broken ones mean 'fold other side', and the fine lines mean 'fold both ways'. To make the folds sharper, draw on them with a very hard pencil (4 or 6H) or score them with a blunt knife along a metal straight-edge. Make sure all lines are parallel and the same distance apart.

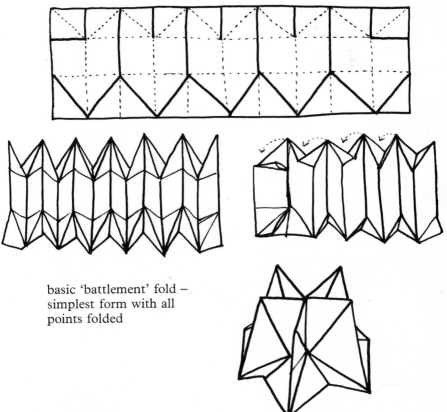

basic 'battlement' fold –
simplest form with all
points folded

Opposite
This yellow hanger is made from folded stiff paper
(see page 60)

Here are three different forms from one basic fold.

Score and fold the paper like this.

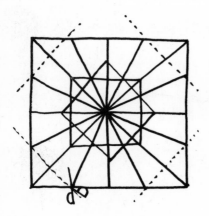

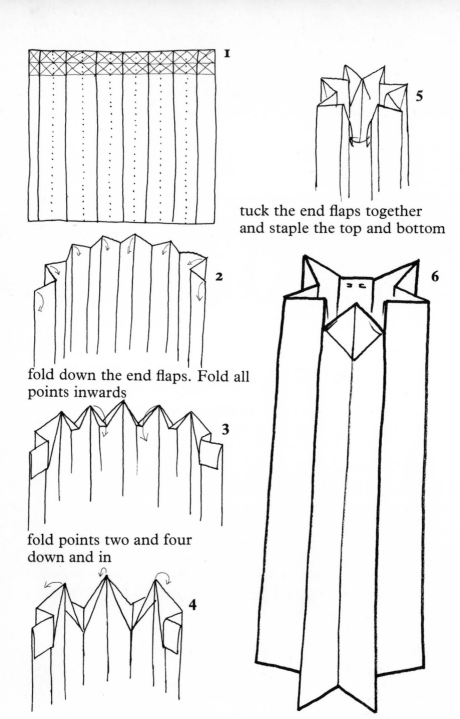

I

2

fold down the end flaps. Fold all points inwards

3

fold points two and four down and in

4

fold the remaining points out and down

5

tuck the end flaps together and staple the top and bottom

6

score and fold the paper
into a concertina shape

turn down alternate points,
starting at the overlap

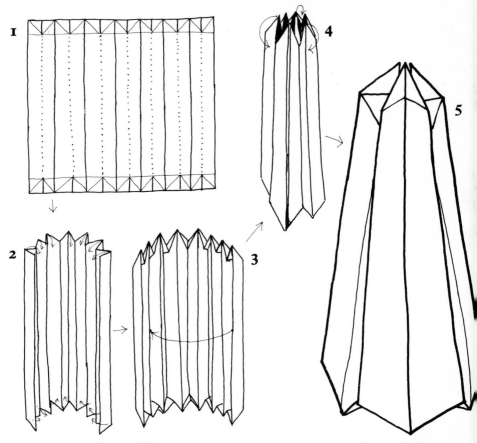

turn in the points at
the top and bottom

overlap the first and
last concertina folds

Architecture

You could make a strange and wonderful city of the future with these shapes. Mount them together on a papier-mâché moon landscape. Here are the folds.

Vaults

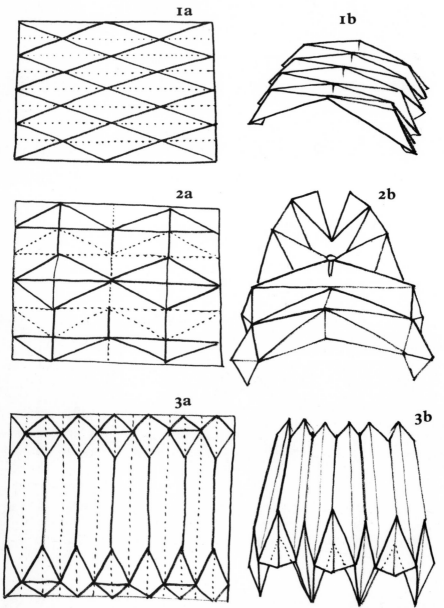

1a

1b

2a

2b

3a

3b

Hangers

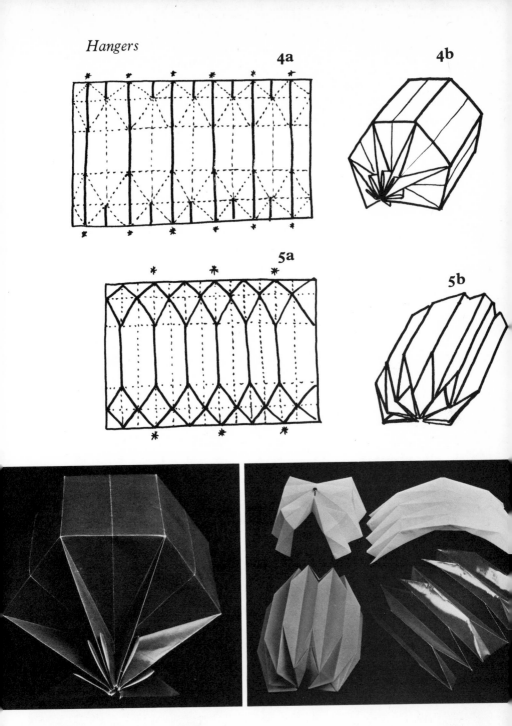

4a

4b

5a

5b

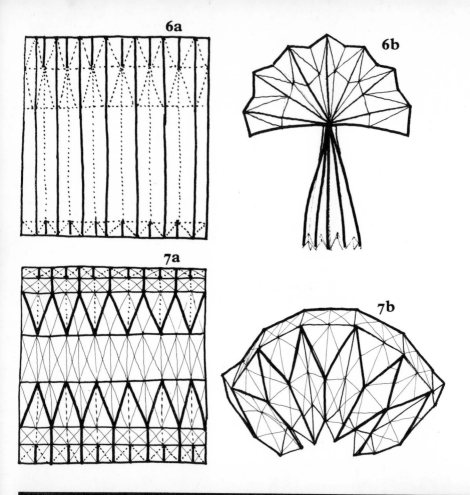

6a

6b

7a

7b

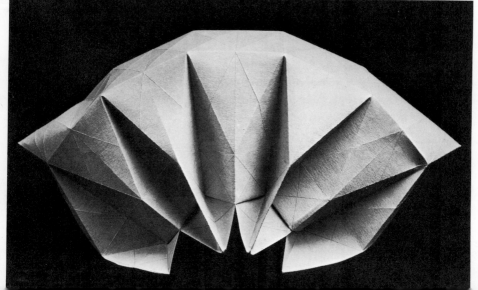

Offcuts and junk

These free abstract sculptures are made from any old offcuts or bits and pieces of paper which you happen to have around. You could use old picture postcards or blank cards that you decorate yourself. Vary the colour as much as you can. Just staple the pieces together.

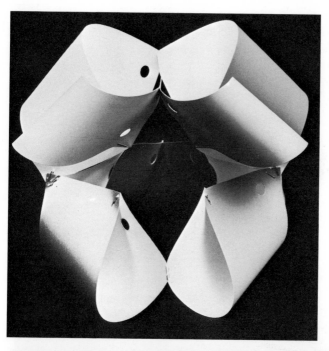

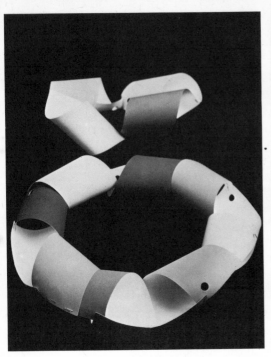

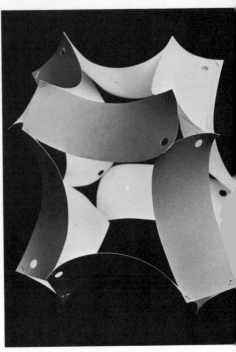

You will find that many sculptures are better hung up than standing and can make nice lampshades.

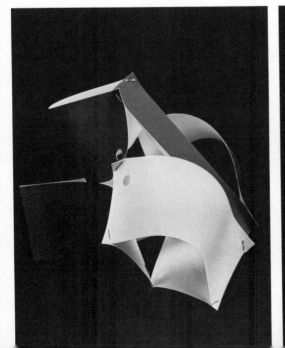

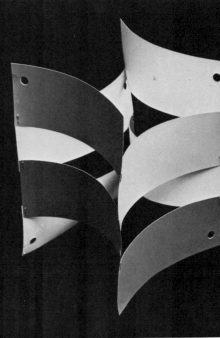

Space frames

The sculptures on the next two pages were all built from giant drinking straws. (They can be bought from craft shops everywhere). The picture below shows one way of joining them with a rubber band. Start with the straws in a bunch, slip the band around them and then spread the straws in all directions. Attach other straws in the same way.

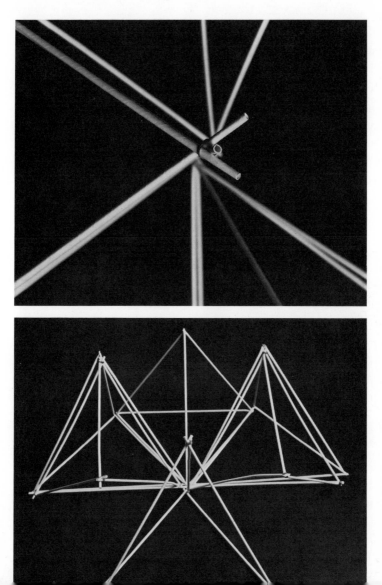

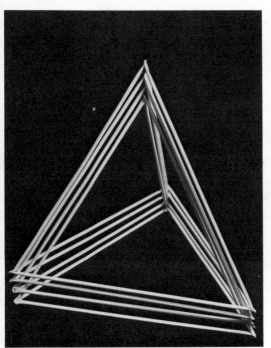

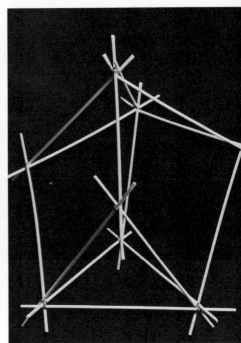

Try making a number of different units. The combinations are almost endless.

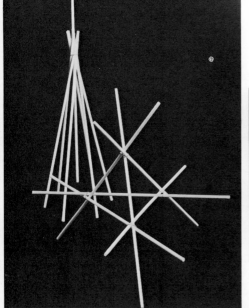

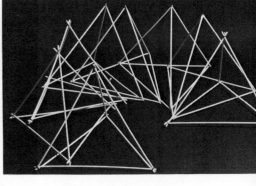

Sound effects

Some good sound effects for the background to plays or recorded drama can be made with paper.

Marching feet – rhythmically crunch up tracing paper.
Gun shot – either burst a blown up paper bag or make a 'snapper' like this.

version 1

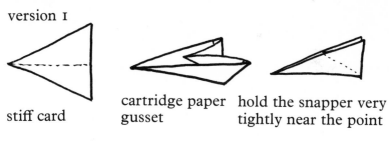

stiff card

cartridge paper gusset

hold the snapper very tightly near the point

swish the snapper through the air and the cartridge gusset will snap out with a loud crack

version 2

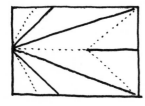

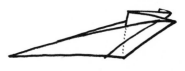

fold the shape from stiff cartridge or brown wrapping paper

For a **whip-crack** (or a distant shot) use a drinking straw.

version I

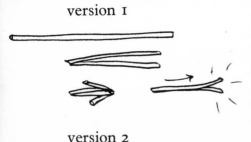

flatten the straw and bend back the ends. Holding the straw, run a finger and thumb sharply along it in the direction of the arrow, so that the ends crack together

version 2

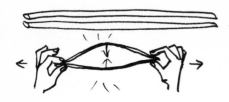

flatten two straws, hold the ends, bow the centres apart, and pull them smartly together

Making music with drinking straws

Cut a short length of a paper drinking straw. Snip the end into this shape with scissors. Put it between your lips so that the cut is inside your mouth. Blow and you will get a high-pitched whistle. The shorter the straw, the higher the pitch. Use a whole straw to make a long one, and pierce holes with a compass point. You will be able to play tunes on it.

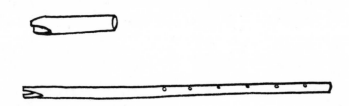

Suppliers

If you decide to buy some special papers for any of your projects, Here are some addresses;

F. J. Kettle
127 High Holborn, London WC1

Paperchase
216 Tottenham Court Road, London W1

Midland Educational
104/106 Corporation Street, Birmingham 4
Branches in Coventry, Northampton, Worcester, Wolverhampton, Leicester, Solihull, Stratford-upon-Avon, Bristol, Shrewsbury.

Arts and Crafts
PO Box 87, 10 Byram Street, Huddersfield, Yorkshire HD1 1DA

Fred Aldous Ltd
37 Lever Street, Manchester, Lancashire, M60 1UX

Millers Arts & Crafts Ltd
54 Queen Street, Glasgow, G1 BDH

Contour Artists Materials Ltd
38 Sandgate, Ayr, Scotland

All the above, except Midland Educational, will supply goods by mail order.
Reeves or Rowneys art shops have good ranges of craft and drawing papers and most stationers will have a selection, though not such a full range as the specialist shops.

Index

abstract sculptures   61
aeroplane   13
architecture   58

balloon   16
bird   9
boats   11

collage   50
cuboctahedron   21, 30

dart   14
die   23
  trick   23
dodecahedron   26, 33
  pop-up   28
drinking straws   66
  giant   63

fiddle cubes   49
flexagons   39
  complex   42, 45, 46
  decorating   47
  square   48

games   17, 36
gun shot   65

hangers   59
hats   15
helicopter   14

icosahedron   29, 30, 32, 33

junk   61

marching feet   65
materials   8
Mobius strip   36
  experiments   37
musical straw   66

newspaper game   17

octahedron   23
offcuts   61
origami   9

paper folding   11
paper sculpture   53
Platonic solids   19
puzzles   36, 20

sculpture   53
sound effects   65
space frames   63
suppliers   67
swan   10

tetrahedron   19
  puzzle   20
  puzzle solution   24
thunder   65
tiger   50
tools   8
towers   56
tricks   18

vaults   58

waterlily   17
whip-crack   65